Written by Catherine Zoller
Pictures by Mr. Sketches

RHYME & REASON SERIES

"GETTING THESE BOOKS IN PEOPLE'S HANDS SO PEOPLE'S HANDS PICK UP THE BOOK."

ABOUT THE AUTHOR

Catherine Zoller is a writer from Tulsa, Oklahoma,
With a husband, three kids, and half a college diploma.

Many years ago the Lord spoke to her one night,
He said simply and clearly, "I want you to write!"

So she jumped out of bed and grabbed paper and a pen,
And waited on the sofa for Him to speak to her again.

At last there came the dawn with the dew and heavy mist,
But all that she had written was half a grocery list.

She never had forgotten all the words she heard that night;
All she had to learn was that His timing's always right.

And so she's written rhymes that tell the Bible story,
From Genesis to Revelation, to reveal God's glory.

The hope within her heart is to show everyone
That reading God's true Word can be a lot of fun!

It will instruct and teach you, and it can change your heart,
And this little book you hold is designed to help you start!

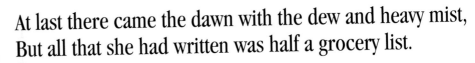

Esther: The Rhyme and Reason Series by Catherine Zoller
Copyright ©2016 by Catherine Zoller
Printed in the Canada

ISBN 978-0-9885122-4-5
For worldwide distribution

Rhyme & Reason Ministries International • P.O. Box 470994 • Tulsa, OK 74147-0994
You can learn more about Catherine Zoller at www.catherinezoller.com

ABOUT THE ILLUSTRATOR

The artist Mr. Sketches is also known by some
As Mr. David Wilson, and he thinks art is fun!

The nickname Mr. Sketches came from a T.V. show
The station TBN broadcast for three years in a row.

His lovely wife named Karen likes to teach the second grade.
They moved around a bit, but when they got to Tulsa stayed.

Art from the heart it surely helps God's children to succeed,
So when he draws and sketches, this is always David's creed:

"With broad point or with fine or whatever time or season,
It's time to draw the line now, whatever rhyme or reason!"

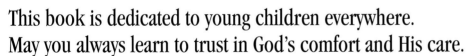

DEDICATION

This book is dedicated to young children everywhere.
May you always learn to trust in God's comfort and His care.

For surely as Queen Esther came, "For such time as this."
There's something only you can do or things will be amiss.

I pray that you will call on Him to show you your life's plan,
And walk with Him all of your days safely hand in hand.

And when you look back on your life, many years from now,
I hope that you give thanks to Him and give a humble bow!

3

The setting of this book is the palace at Shushan;
It's one of the three capitals within the Persian land.

The tension builds until it looks like things are out of hand.
Yet we learn that no condition is beyond our God's command.

His name is never mentioned once as this true tale unfolds,
And yet He works behind the scenes, His purpose to uphold.

And so then what's at stake, the reader very well may ask?
Why, just the fate of all the Jews in evil Haman's grasp!

But as He always does, God takes the humble not the proud,
And uses them to do His will in ways that leave us wowed.

He took a lovely orphan girl, probably still a teen,
And through her brave obedience, God's plan is plainly seen.

In His loving providence He's sure to make a way,
To triumph over evil and let goodness save the day.

From then till now the feast of Purim comes again each year.
The book of Esther read aloud for young and old to hear.

The reading of the megillah (scroll) is quite a big affair.
Dressed in costumes, people act the story out with flair.

Each time ol' Haman's name comes up the people yell and boo!
And when it's over they rejoice that God had seen them through.

They eat triangle cookies filled with sesame seed goo;
Send gifts to one another and the poor are helped out, too.

The triangle treat reminds them of the shape of Haman's hat,
Worn within the Persian Court by all the old fat cats.

So gather around and listen now as Esther's read to you.
Try to imagine what you'd do if you were in her shoes.

Remember as you listen that you've a destiny, too;
So pray and ask, "Please, Lord, just how can I serve you?"

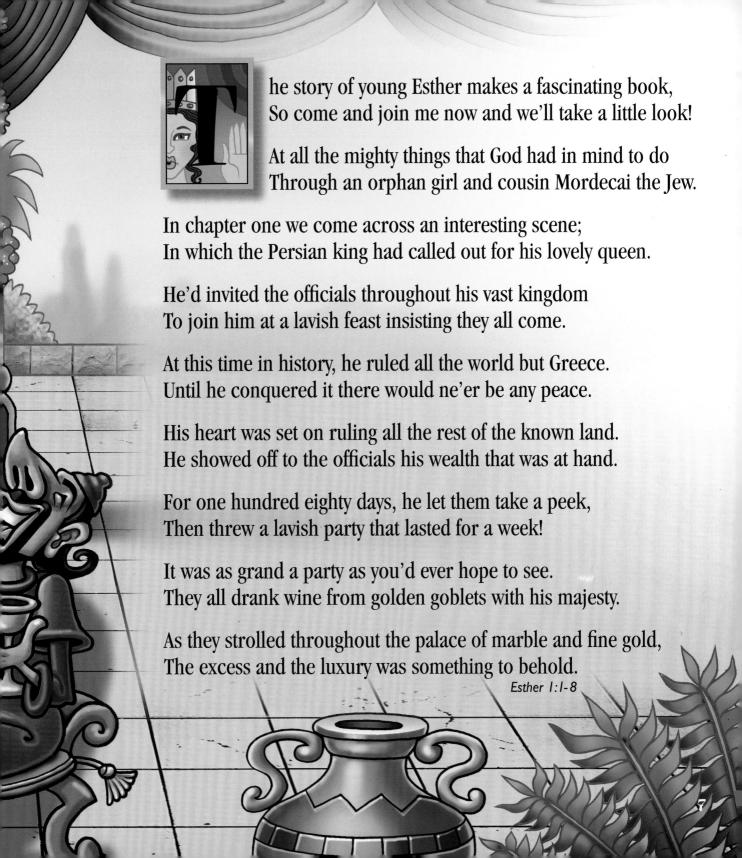

The story of young Esther makes a fascinating book,
So come and join me now and we'll take a little look!

At all the mighty things that God had in mind to do
Through an orphan girl and cousin Mordecai the Jew.

In chapter one we come across an interesting scene;
In which the Persian king had called out for his lovely queen.

He'd invited the officials throughout his vast kingdom
To join him at a lavish feast insisting they all come.

At this time in history, he ruled all the world but Greece.
Until he conquered it there would ne'er be any peace.

His heart was set on ruling all the rest of the known land.
He showed off to the officials his wealth that was at hand.

For one hundred eighty days, he let them take a peek,
Then threw a lavish party that lasted for a week!

It was as grand a party as you'd ever hope to see.
They all drank wine from golden goblets with his majesty.

As they strolled throughout the palace of marble and fine gold,
The excess and the luxury was something to behold.

Esther 1:1-8

7

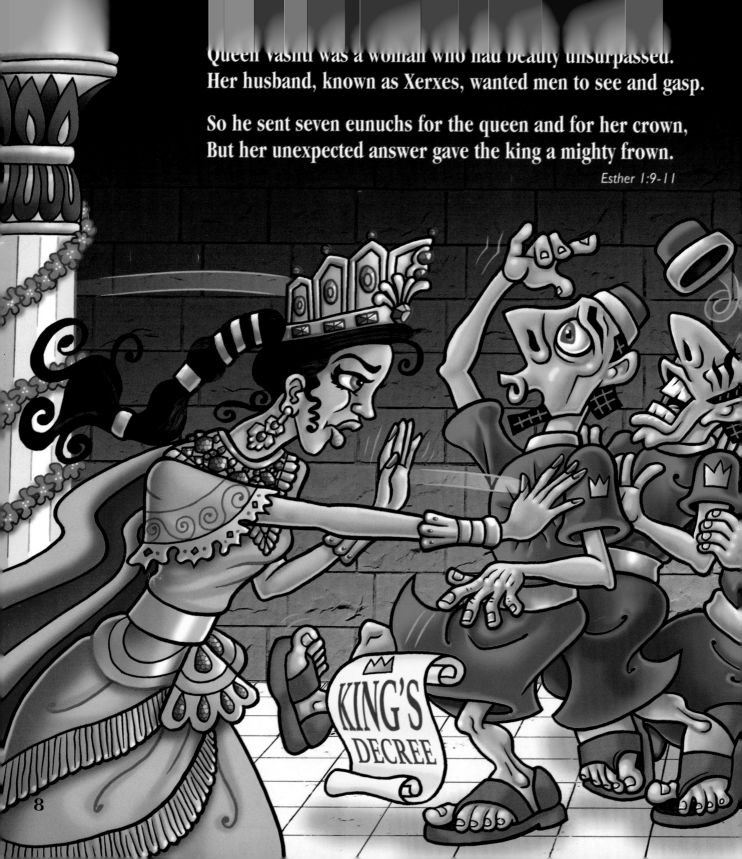

Queen Vashti was a woman who had beauty unsurpassed.
Her husband, known as Xerxes, wanted men to see and gasp.

So he sent seven eunuchs for the queen and for her crown,
But her unexpected answer gave the king a mighty frown.

Esther 1:9-11

KING'S DECREE

8

Now you might be surprised by what quickly happens here,
When Vashti told the eunuchs she wouldn't bother to appear.

You see, Vashti was quite busy with a party of her own;
Refusing to be summoned for the sake of being shown.

Esther 1:12

When the servants told the king
    the queen refused to come,
The king was filled with angry wrath
    and fit to be undone.

You see, back in those ancient days
    it simply was not fitting,
Even for the royal queen
    to scorn her monarch's bidding.

So he asked all his wise men
    what he should do that day
About the problem of a queen
    who dared to disobey.

Now it might seem to us
    that they overreact a bit;
But we must try and understand
    an important fact—to wit:

The rules back then were different
    than the rules we have today.
In 483 BC,
    this position seemed okay.

The officials feared the women
    all throughout the lands
Would disregard their husbands,
    disobeying their commands.

Esther 1:13-18

QUEEN
VASHTI

KING
XERXES

11

A royal decree was crafted, which soon became the law,
That Vashti now be banished and a better woman sought.

Beautiful Queen Vashti never saw the king again.
A second decree was issued—that women honor men.

Esther 1:19-22

When he'd finally calmed back down,
servants said unto the king,
"Let us search throughout the land
for beautiful young things."

MISS T R

This solution pleased the king;
    he gave the royal "Yes!"
To find young virgins they could shape
    and beautify and dress.

And so they gathered maidens
    who were lovely and so heady,
Then took an entire year to get them
    beautified and ready.   Esther 2:1-4

young Jewess named Hadassah was among those whom they found.
We know her now as Esther, a young maid who'd stand her ground.

The Lord gave her great favor with the servants of the court,
So she was pampered and perfumed as if it were a sport.

Esther 2:8-9

16

A tidbit in this true tale
    that I tell with a warm sigh;
Young Esther had been raised
    by her cousin Mordecai.

You see, both of her parents died
    and left her all alone.
So Mordecai stepped in
    and he raised her as his own.

They needed one another,
    and they had a special bond
That comes to play in a way
    that we'll see later on.

At first Esther did not reveal
    her family or her race
As Mordecai instructed when
    he last saw her face.

And every day he paced and paced
    outside the women's court,
To learn of Esther's welfare and
    to try and lend support.

Esther 2:5-7; 10-11

18

One at a time, each woman took
 a turn before the king.
And from the women's court,
 she could take with her anything.

She'd go there in the morning,
 in the evening she'd go back;
Another would be chosen
 so that she could take a crack.

Esther 2:12-14

19

Finally it was Esther's turn; the eunuch told her what to bring.
And oh! The king he loved her so; she made his sad heart sing!

Esther 2:15

20

The king then held a feast for her and called it by her name;
With countless invitations and a holiday proclaimed.

Esther 2:17-18

21

 nd then one day, Mordecai heard, while sitting at the gate,
Of a plot to kill the king by two eunuchs filled with hate.

He quickly told Queen Esther and sweet Esther told the king.
These two men were soon captured; from the gallows they did swing.

23

One day Xerxes promoted Haman over other men.
The king told all the people to bow down and honor him.

Mordecai refused to bow—he was a righteous Jew.
All the other servants bowed, they asked, "So why don't you?"

He told them all the truth: he was a faithful Jew.
Then these told wicked Haman, who began to seethe and stew.

He got so angry, he resolved that every Jew would die!
Because his pride was wounded by our faithful Mordecai.

Esther 3:1-7

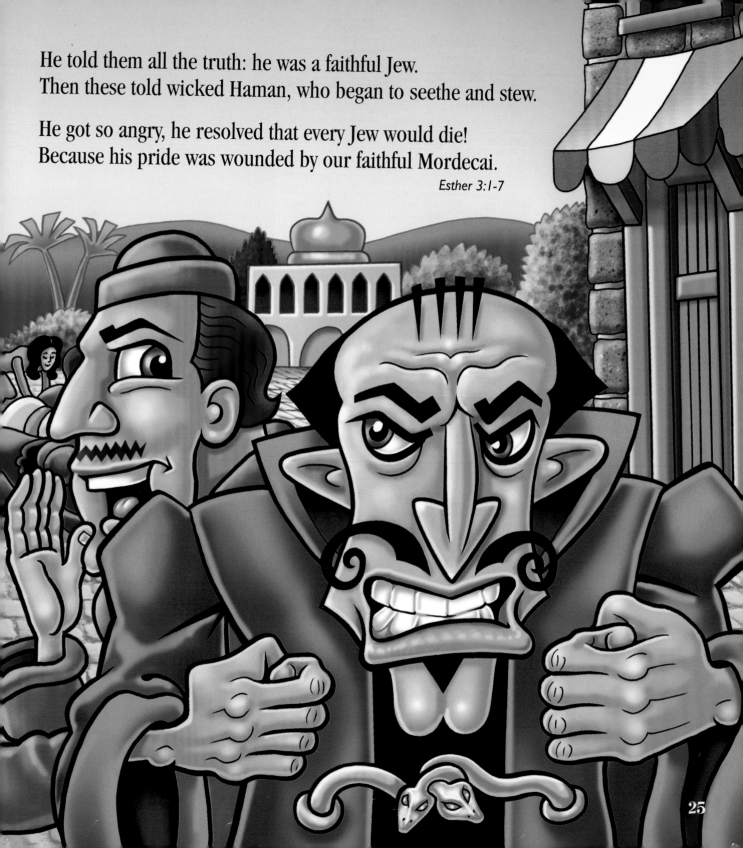

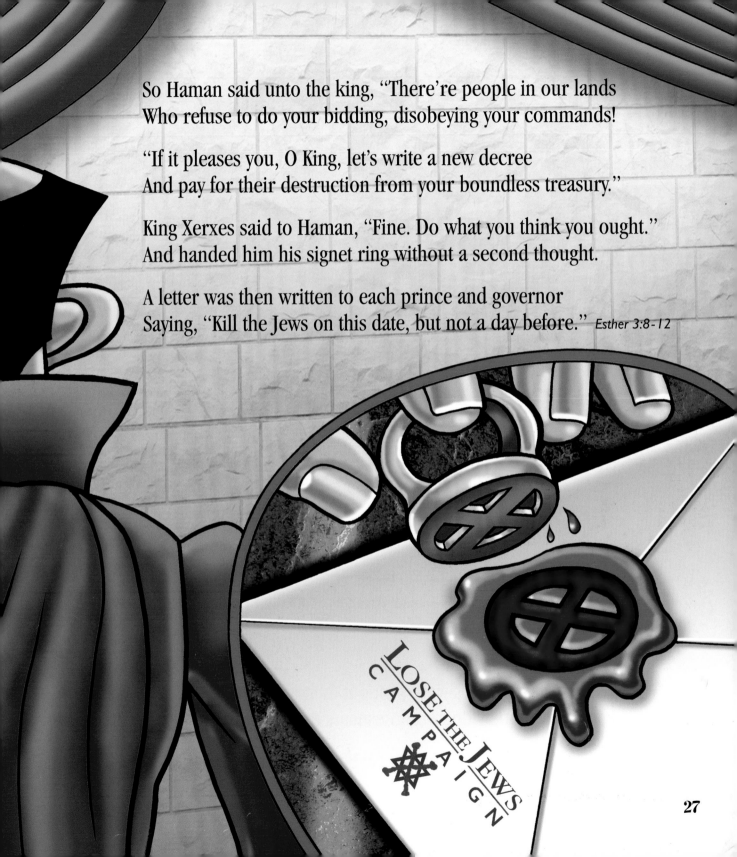

So Haman said unto the king, "There're people in our lands
Who refuse to do your bidding, disobeying your commands!

"If it pleases you, O King, let's write a new decree
And pay for their destruction from your boundless treasury."

King Xerxes said to Haman, "Fine. Do what you think you ought."
And handed him his signet ring without a second thought.

A letter was then written to each prince and governor
Saying, "Kill the Jews on this date, but not a day before." *Esther 3:8-12*

LOSE THE JEWS CAMPAIGN

The couriers were sent out then to spread the king's commands,
With their decrees to execute the Jews throughout his lands.

When at last ol' Mordecai heard what had taken place,
He tore his clothes in mourning and he fell down on his face.

He wore sackcloth and ashes and went around the city,
Weeping, wailing, crying out for justice and for pity.

In each and every province when the king's decree was read,
The people wept and wailed, and their hearts were filled with dread.

Esther 3:13- 4:3

When Esther's maidens told her,
    the queen became distressed.
She sent ol' Mordecai new clothes
    so he could get redressed.

But he would not accept them,
    and he kept his mourning clothes.
She sent her servant out to ask
    her uncle of his woes.

Then Mordecai relayed to him
    the things Haman had done;
His evil plan to kill the Jews,
    to spare not even one.

He handed him a copy of
    the newly writ decree,
To show to lovely Esther
    so that she might make a plea.

He hoped she'd go before the king
    and for her people plea.
But she reminded Mordecai
    that the king must first agree.

"Everyone within the land
    knows one law to be true:
If you go before the king
    who hasn't summoned you,

"Good chance you will be put to death
     unless he will extend
His golden scepter out to you—
     for then your life won't end.

"And I myself have not been called
     for these last thirty days."
So back to Mordecai they went
     and these words were relayed.

He told the servant, "Tell my niece,
     'Don't think that you'll be spared.
For if you do not act, then help will
     still come from somewhere.

'You and your father's house will perish
     lest you take the risk.
For who knows whether you are queen
     for such a time as this?'"

Then Esther told them to reply
     to cousin Mordecai,
"Gather all the Jews and fast
     'til three days have gone by.

"I'll gather all my maidens
     and we'll fast and pray and cry,
And then I'll go before the king
     and if I die, I die."   *Esther 4:4-17*

She donned her royal robes and she prayed with all her might.
The king held out his scepter; she'd found favor in his sight.

He said to her, "What's troubling you, and what is your request?"
"Oh, please" she said, "I'd ask that you and Haman be my guests.

"I have prepared a banquet and I'd like you both to come."
The king agreed, he summoned Haman, and the deed was done.

Esther 5:1-4

Once there, he asked his wife,
    "What is it you'd like done?
I tell you I will grant it,
    up to half of my kingdom!"

"If it please the king once more
    to do what I'll ask of you,
Come to another banquet and,
    oh, please bring Haman, too.

"I'll tell you after dinner
    my petition and request."
The king agreed, the three departed,
    off to get some rest.

Now Haman was beside himself,
    his heart was truly glad,
But when he passed by Mordecai,
    he went from glad to mad.

He walked on home to find his wife
    and tell her everything,
And bragged to all his friends of his
    good fortune with the king.

Esther 5:5-11

34

"Even Esther let no one dine with the king but me.
Again tomorrow I'll be there in both their company.

"Yet none of this does satisfy and I become irate,
Every time I pass that Jew who's sitting at the gate."

His wife and friends all said to him,
    "Then have a gallows made,
And ask the king to hang the man
    who turns your face this shade!

"That way you can go in peace to
    your feasting with the king."
This advice quite pleased Haman,
    and so he built the thing.

Esther 5:12-14

Late that night the king lay tossing,
    turning in his bed,
He gave an order for the books
    of records to be read.

And it was found that Mordecai
    had heard the eunuch's plot
To make their way up to the king
    and kill him on the spot.

He asked those who attended him,
    "What honor has been shown
To the man who saved my life
    with no thought of his own?"

They told him nothing had been done,
    then heard a noise close by.
"Who is that who's in my court?"
    It was Haman who was nigh.

He'd come to ask the king to string up
    Mordecai the Jew,
But was surprised when Xerxes asked,
    "What now would you do?

What should be done to honor one
    the king desires to praise?"
Haman, of course, was sure the king
    had him within his gaze.

Esther 6:1-6

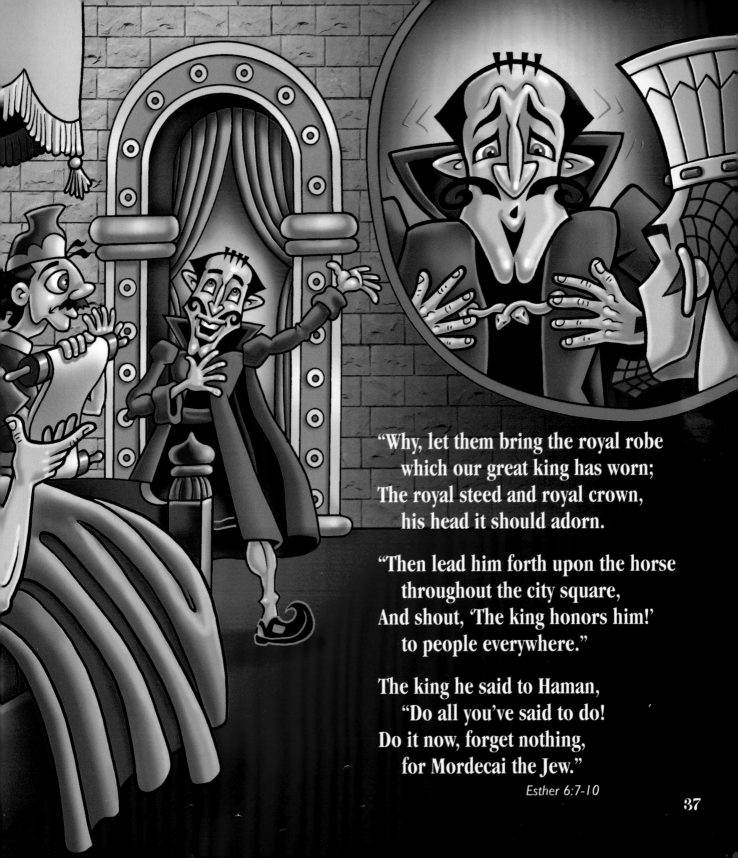

"Why, let them bring the royal robe
which our great king has worn;
The royal steed and royal crown,
his head it should adorn.

"Then lead him forth upon the horse
throughout the city square,
And shout, 'The king honors him!'
to people everywhere."

The king he said to Haman,
"Do all you've said to do!
Do it now, forget nothing,
for Mordecai the Jew."

Esther 6:7-10

So Haman took the robe and crown to honor Mordecai.
He led him through the city streets, his voice was lifted high.

"Thus shall it be done for him whom Xerxes wants to praise!"
Then Haman hurried to his home in shame, his eyes ablaze.

His wife and friends all said to him, "In this you can't prevail.
If you stand against this man, then you are bound to fail."

And while they were still speaking, the king's eunuchs came for him,
To take him to the banquet Esther had prepared for them. *Esther 6:11-14*

And as he'd done now once before,
   the king implored his queen,
"What is it you would ask of me;
   I'll give you anything."

"O King, my people have been sold
   to be destroyed and killed!
All of this has happened due
   to what one man has willed.

"If we were simply sold as slaves,
   I would have held my tongue,
Though we would still have suffered,
   men and women, old and young."

King Xerxes, now quite angry, asked,
   "Who made this wicked plan?"
She said, "The one who sits before you—
   Haman is the man!" *Esther 7:1-6*

In his wrath the king arose and stepped into the garden.
While Haman threw himself on Esther, begging for a pardon.

When the king returned, he found him on the couch with Esther,
He said, "Will he also assault my queen, trying to molest her?"

"Look out there," a eunuch cried. "Gallows fifty cubits high!
The very one on which he planned to hang dear Mordecai!"

In his wrath the king cried out,
  "Make haste and hang him now!"
And so when Haman kicked his last
  the king relaxed his brow. Esther 7:7-10

41

hen King Xerxes gave his queen
all Haman's fine estate.
Then Esther told how Mordecai's
faithfulness was great.

And so the king gave Mordecai
his shiny signet ring,
And Esther gave him power over
all of Haman's things.

Then Esther fell upon the ground,
right at her husband's feet,
Begging him with tears to stop
the Jews' coming defeat.

The king held out his scepter and
the queen, she rose and stood,
And asked him to change the law
from evil unto good.

"For how can I endure to see
this evil edict come,
And see my people soon destroyed,
not sparing anyone?" *Esther 8:1-6*

42

So Xerxes said to both of them,
  "Go write a new decree.
Then seal it with my signet ring
  as if it came from me.

"For what is written in my name
  no one can e'er revoke."
The scribes were called, a new law signed,
  by a single stylus stroke.   *Esther 8:7-9*

To every province in the land,
    out went royal decrees.
Couriers delivered letters
    riding royal steeds.

Each was written in the language
    that the people spoke.
And once the law had been declared,
    it could not be revoked.

In these letters it was clear,
    Jews could protect their lives,
Including those of all their children
    and their Jewish wives.

The king adorned our hero in
    the colors of his land;
In blue and white apparel
    with fine linen purple band.

Esther 8:10-15

44

The king's favor was upon him
and his pleasure was displayed,
By the golden crown and clothing
in which he was arrayed.

In each and every province where
the king's command was read,
Joy and gladness filled the Jews,
replacing all the dread.

Because of this deliverance now
others became Jews!
Feasts were held to celebrate
all this exciting news.

Esther 8:16-17

At last the day arrived when the first edict took effect,
But all who hoped to kill the Jews were forced to redirect.

Instead of taking Jewish lives, turns out they lost their own.
No one could withstand the Jews; their strength was surely shown.

Mordecai became quite great; his fame spread throughout the land,
And, with others who held power, helped the Jews to take a stand.

For two days they avenged themselves and rose up to the call.
They killed the sons of Haman who numbered ten in all. *Esther 9:1-15*

They conquered all their enemies and those who hated them,
And then they put their weapons down and brought it to an end.

When they finally rested, there was feasting and great gladness.
The feast of Purim was declared which put an end to sadness.

A custom was established that extends down to today,
To celebrate this two day feast, the story to replay.

They read the book of Esther and recall their history,
So these events that came to pass stay in their memory. *Esther 9:16-19*

Even though this story doesn't
    one time mention God,
We see His sovereign hand at work
    and can't help but be awed.

Now let this be a lesson
    that if God is on your side,
He will work behind the scenes
    to preserve, prepare, provide!